EULALIE'S JOURNEY TO ALGONQUIN
with TOM THOMSON

A Collaboration of Words and Imagery by

Catherine Wilson & Ruth MacLean

Published by Ailsapress 2018
Port Charlotte Isle of Islay PA48 7TS UK
www.ailsapress.com

ISBN 978-0-9954912-1-2
Text © Catherine Wilson Illustrations © Ruth MacLean

Also by Catherine Wilson and Ruth MacLean
THE TAIL OF AILSA 2007
BRAMBLE AND COULTOON Their Hebridean Adventure 2009
BRAMBLE AND COULTOON Their Sky Dragon Adventure 2011
BRAMBLE AND COULTOON Their Bolsa Cave Adventure 2014

Printed and bound in Canada by Friesens on acid free paper
Distributed in Canada by Georgetown Publications L7G 4R9 Ontario

In gratitude to the Tom Thomson Gallery, Owen Sound

There are so many "withouts" in the coming together of this book. Without Ruth returning to visit Islay, the Scottish island of her grandfather's birth; without Ruth meeting Cathy in Islay; without years passing and a steadfast friendship; without the serendipity of an encounter at the Tom Thomson Gallery, this book would not have come into being.

It was Suzanne Watson of the Tom Thomson Gallery who sowed the seed with her imaginative suggestion, "Why don't you two do a book about Tom Thomson and his dog?"

We are most grateful to the whole team at the Gallery. They make visible the story of Tom Thomson's life in the region to which he belonged. We hope that this book adds another small flavour to the medley of colour, canvas and archive material at the Gallery.

A bouquet of Tom Thomson flowers!
Ruth's image is based on Tom Thomson's
Mocassin Flower painted in Spring 1916
Private Collection, Toronto.

Tom Thomson at Lake Scugog, Fall 1910
T.H. Marten Black and White Photograph; Collection of the Tom Thomson Art Gallery, Owen Sound. Gift of Margaret Murch, 1998.

INTRODUCTION
Tom Thomson's Life

Tom Thomson had a dog and her name was Eulalie. Very little is known about his dog besides the one photograph taken in 1910 that shows Tom at the end of a dock on Lake Scugog with Eulalie beside him. So Eulalie's story of her time with Tom is imaginary in many ways. Yet it is also based on definite facts in Tom's life.

Tom did have a shack in Toronto where he painted in the winter months; he could easily have taken Eulalie for walks in the nearby Rosedale Valley; he did take the train from Toronto to reach Algonquin; and while in Algonquin, he fished, he camped and painted many landscape subjects. The wolf in the story was also real to Tom. There is a letter written after his death by his sister Louise whose husband had asked Tom if he was not afraid of the wild animals in the wilderness:

> *"Why," [Tom] said, "the animals are our friends. I've picked raspberries on one side of a log while a big black bear picked berries on the other side. He also told him of one time he was tramping through the woods when he heard some animal coming towards him through the undergrowth and to his surprise it was a large timber wolf, one of the largest he had ever seen, its head, neck and breast were jet black and the body the usual grey color. He said it was the most beautiful animal he had ever seen. The wolf came so close to him he could almost have touched him with his hand ... ."*
> Louise Henry to Blodwen Davies March 11 1931 [LAC Blodwen Davies fonds:C-4579]

Finally Tom did die in mysterious circumstances on Canoe Lake and there is a lot of speculation about what may have happened. Many people insist that there was foul play. The truth is that no one will ever know.

We have tried to weave Tom's paintings of Algonquin into the story in a way that fits with what is known about his life. Every now and then we have taken a liberty, for instance, we have placed the picture that shows Tom and Eulalie at the end of the dock at Canoe Lake, not at Lake Scugog.

From his earliest years, Tom loved to be in nature. His home was on the shores of Georgian Bay and as a youngster he and his brothers were often taken for nature walks with their "uncle", a well-known biologist called Dr William Brodie. Tom felt at home in nature. He knew the different plants and trees, and the different creatures. He was a great swimmer and he loved to fish. Later when he introduced his fellow artists to Algonquin, they were very impressed by his ability to catch and cook fish on an open fire, or steer a canoe along rapids.

It was not obvious what Tom wanted to do when he grew up. In fact, he seems to have been in a bit of a muddle about it. When he was 21 he came into a legacy of some $2000 left to him by his grandfather. He used some of this money to attend a college at Chatham where he started a business study course like two of his brothers before him. Soon he followed the same two brothers to Seattle. Here he got a job as a graphic designer working in the field of advertising. He had no training as such but was good at learning from the example of others. He was altogether three years in Seattle but left abruptly. He had fallen in love with a girl eight years his junior. When he proposed marriage to her, apparently the young girl giggled. Probably she was nervous but Tom was so shocked he never tried to see her again.

By June of 1905 we know that Tom was back in Canada. He was now 27 years old but there was still no sign that Tom would ever become a painter. In 1908 he joined a Toronto print firm called Grip Ltd., where he met for the first time a group of artists some of whom would become members of the famous "Group of Seven". In 1912 he went on two expeditions to Algonquin Park, the first in the spring with painter Ben Jackson, and the second in the fall on a two month canoeing trip with painter William Broadhead. His sister Louise recounts:

> *"One story he told was of a very narrow escape he and Mr. Broadhead had while running a rapids with the canoe pretty well loaded with supplies and their season's sketches. The canoe struck on a submerged rock and they lost most of their best sketches, most of their supplies, and came very nearly losing their lives. Mr. Broadhead said that if Tom had not been such an expert canoesman, they would both have been lost."*
> Louise Henry to Blodwen Davies March 11 1931 [LAC Blodwen Davies fonds:C-4579]

These two trips to Algonquin in 1912 marked the beginning of Tom's career as a painter. In fact it is quite extraordinary how many paintings he made in the short five-year span that remained of his life. You would even say that the accident on the canoe trip created a sense of urgency for Tom. Any person studying Tom's brush marks can see their immediacy. Hesitation does not seem to have been in Tom's vocabulary when it came to act of painting.

Ruth MacLean, the artist who has created the paper collages of Tom's paintings for this book, describes her experience in these words:

> It is Tom's excitement and intimacy with nature that makes him so special. I myself have spent nights under the stars and I love to see the changing light as dawn comes, or feel the breeze off the lake. I could really resonate with Tom when I was making the paper images - and I couldn't tear myself away. I sometimes started at seven in the morning and went on till eleven at night. Because Tom lived in nature, he noticed the intimate details. You notice all these things, you start seeing every little thing, and it becomes a revelation.

Mark Robinson, Chief Ranger in Algonquin at the time of Tom's visits, gives us an enduring description of Tom's dedication to colour:

> "... we were looking at an old Pine stump that was partially covered with moss and the grey colour of the wood was of many shades of grey. He looked at it and said there is one of the hardest things to paint in the woods. See those different shades of grey. [An] artist must get them in perfect or the sketch is a fraud on the Public - there aren't more than two or three in every hundred who will notice it but its not true to nature and imperfect notes destroy the soul of music so does imperfect colour destroy the soul of the canvas."
> Mark Robinson to Blodwen Davies March 23 1930 [LAC Blodwen Davies fonds:C-4579]

In our story, Eulalie's discovery that Tom is trying to catch the light is the equivalent to his "catching the colour". We wanted to be careful about Eulalie's capacity to see colour because in fact dogs have much less colour vision than we do. As two human beings blessed with colour vision, we are convinced that it was Tom's incredible capacity to see and draw with colour that made him the unique artist that he was and will always remain.

Catherine Wilson Isle of Islay, Scotland
Ruth MacLean Kincardine, Ontario
January 2018

TORONTO

My story begins when Tom visited the house where I was born. I had seven brothers and sisters but one by one they all went away and I was the only one left. I heard them speaking with Tom. They told him that I was the runt of the litter. Tom said, "Not a bit of it, she's a little treasure and she can come painting with me!"

Tom picked me up and snuggled me against his chest. I was in love with him already and I liked the funny smell he had. I didn't know what it was at first.

Tom's house had the same smell that Tom had. It was a mixture of things. For sure it had to do with the funny thing he put in his mouth. I called it his mouth-stick. Sometimes he took a very tiny stick and did something with it. Usually it burst into a flame, but not always. Then Tom made smoke come out of his mouth. It was magic!

Tom had a game with sticks. Sadly he didn't play this game with me but he didn't mind if I sat in the corner and watched. He spent a long time mixing a kind of oily paste. It wasn't the kind of paste you could eat. "No, little treasure, you won't like that but try it and see."

Anyway, Tom made lots of different patches of this paste and then he did the strangest thing. He put his sticks into the paste and then pasted the paste on to a "canvas". I knew the name for this because he was always saying, "Now just be careful of my canvas, my canvas is my life!" So I knew his CANVAS was important to him.

The paste he used for his canvas was the other smell on Tom and in his house. I could always smell Tom from a long way off. I loved him.

Myself I preferred to play with bigger sticks.

My favourite time was when Tom and I went for walks together. He took me to the woods near our home. I loved it when Tom picked up a stick and threw it and I ran as fast as I could and picked it up and took it back to him. I couldn't wait till he threw the stick again.

I could have played all day fetching sticks for Tom. But I knew that after a while, Tom got homesick for his own sticks. We would go back to his studio and he would paste another canvas.

Tom had a lot of little people friends. They liked to visit him. The little people wanted to know my name. Tom said, "She's my little treasure." "You mean," they asked, "Her name is Little Treasure?"

"Well," said Tom. "I'm not quite sure. Sure she is a little treasure, but I haven't thought of a proper name for her. Hey, what do you think, little people, what's a good name for my little treasure? You tell me!"

"You-tell-me that's her name," said one bright spark.

"No," said Tom, "that's almost right, but not quite right. Think of something that kind of rhymes and is much prettier!"

So that's how I came to be called Eulalie.

One day Tom told me, "Eulalie, we're going camping!" I watched Tom fill up boxes. He packed up his paste box with his paste sticks, and a pile of wooden panels. There was one big piece of blue material that he stretched out on the ground, and folded over and over until it got small enough that he could fit it into another box. Later I found out it was the most important part of our "camping" trip. It was our tent.

Tom, his boxes and I then got on to a train. When it moved, I saw everything disappearing behind us and I thought we might be going to the very edge of the world. Tom didn't seem worried. Every now and then he lit up his mouth stick, or gave me some water and a pat.

A

LGONQUIN PARK
It took us almost a day to go where we were going. We were going north where there was water, water, everywhere. I didn't know why, but Tom was quieter here. He spent a lot of time just looking over the water. So did I.

This was Canoe Lake. I never got tired of looking at the water. If I ever came back to Algonquin, it would be to sit beside Canoe Lake. Here I wondered about what makes things move the way they do. I knew that the wind had something to do with it but that wasn't all. There was something beyond the wind.

One day there was no wind. The water was glassy still and the ice had almost all melted. Tom and I went to the end of the dock. He took out his mouth-stick and sent out his magic signals. After a while he stopped. He just stood there very quiet, not even speaking to me.

Meantime I was looking at another dog in the water. Tom bent down and said, "Eulalie, do you know who that is? That's you, look!" He put out his hand and ruffled the water and the dog disappeared. When the water was still again, Tom laughed. "Eulalie, my little treasure, you've come back again!"

Tom taught me many things. He knew how to catch my attention.

I felt like a very special dog when Tom took me out on the lake.

I sat at the front of the canoe while Tom used a very big stick to pull the water and push the boat forward. I loved to sit and watch the water swishing. Then Tom stopped and took out a very long thin stick. At the end of it dangled a long thin tail. I think the tail must have had eyes, and could see underwater. Anyway, when Tom pulled it up, there was often a fish on it.

One night, we could see the tips of the spruce trees pointing into a silvery blue sky. It looked almost like moonlight but it wasn't. Tom said to me, "Eulalie, come, we're going to see the greatest show on earth."

He sat me close to him so we could keep each other warm. There was still a nip in the air.

"Eulalie. See! It's begun, the shooting of the light, it's light firing light."* We sat there watching the silent soaring play for a long time. I knew, this was the love song of the great Sky God.

This play of light is known as the Aurora Borealis, or the Northern Lights.

When it got warmer, we moved out from the lodge by Canoe Lake. We followed the shore until we got to a clearing. Tom said to me, "Go and see what you can find, Eulalie! When you come back, I'll have a fancy new home for us, just you wait and see!"

So off I went to smell all the new smells. I found all sorts of smells, but not of any other dogs. And there were none of Tom's people either. I was the only dog, and Tom was the only man.

That evening Tom made a campfire and grilled us two fish. He boned them and gave me one all to myself. I was tired out and Tom the same. "Come on, Eulalie, time for bed," he said. "Let's retire to our new home!" I lay awake for a while listening to the sounds of the night, but soon I was asleep beside Tom. He snored.

In the middle of the night, I woke. I heard my wolf-cousins. They were howling. I could see them in my mind's eye, their necks craned back and their noses pointing to the stars. They were making their star talk. I remembered that a long time ago, we dogs came from the same race.

This was before we left the pack and before we became friendly with people.

In the morning, Tom got busy with his paste sticks. It was early. The sun was still low and lighting up the water. All around us, it was still dark.

Suddenly I understood what Tom was doing. This was a big moment for me. I understood why Tom pasted. He was catching the light. I could see the water catching the light, and how Tom was catching the light on the water.

We stayed in our new home for days and days. I was so happy. Tom caught more and more light, and he caught fish too. I got to catch all sorts of new smells.

I met some of my new brothers and sisters. The beavers were my favourite. They had amazing teeth and I saw how they cut down trees.

Every night I heard my cousins. Once in the daytime and I was in a clearing amongst all the lovely flowers, suddenly I smelled Him. I stayed stock still and put my nose in the air. I knew he was near but he didn't show himself. One day I knew I would meet Him and it would be with Tom.

On one of my jaunts I found another big lake. At the edge of the lake, there was a big pine tree and just beneath it a hollow in the ground where I could fit snugly and lie down and take shelter from the wind. I thought this would be a good place for Tom to catch the light. So I barked. Tom usually came when I barked, he knew it was my way of calling him.

Sure enough Tom found me. "My goodness, Eulalie, I do believe you have discovered this spot just for me. You're a genius, and if you were a person, you would definitely be a good park guide."

I was proud of myself when Tom said that. He often came back to this spot to catch the light.

One day we went again to the pine tree at the edge of the lake. It was very very windy. I could hear the tree creaking in the wind and I didn't want to lie beneath it. Tom got out his paste sticks and started to paste his panel. I watched him carefully, I didn't want anything bad to happen. When Tom was in the middle of catching the light, he didn't take much notice of anything else. It was me who warned him. I barked and I barked as I saw the tree falling. It fell with a tremendous crash. Tom got out of the way just in time. He put his hand on my muzzle. "Thank you, Eulalie, you saved my life!"

There are some things it is difficult to translate from dog language. I just hoped Tom knew I loved him to his dying day.

Tom said, "Come on, my girl, let's arise and go now. We have three trout for our supper!"

Soon after the windy day, we moved camp. Tom found another clearing by the shore where the fishing was good. The weather was getting warmer all the time. Sometimes the black flies bothered us a lot. At other times, the clouds gathered in gigantic furls that looked too big for their own good. Then came a flash and a roar from the great sky spirit.

I hid in the tent. Nothing would persuade me to leave until the pelting rain had stopped its drumming. But I knew that the rain gave so much back to the earth. The flowers sparkled, the bees hummed, and the little creatures of the forest grew bigger day by day.

We dogs are always afraid of the Sky God's anger.

I was hoping for another day's fishing but Tom said, "Little do you know, Eulalie, but I paint for our supper too!" So he pasted all day.

We were walking back to our tent, when we met Him. I was in front of Tom when my nose picked up his scent. I stood pointing in his direction.

"Hey, little girl, what's up?"

I didn't move because I knew he was coming. Tom stood still too, waiting. Then my Big Cousin stood right before us. His eyes took me in first, then Tom. I was shaking inside but it was not from fear. It was from the shock of seeing Him whom I had known for so long and yet had never seen. It was like greeting the winter in spring time.

My Big Cousin then stalked past us with his dark tail held high.

In those last days we spent a lot of time together. I never let Tom out of my sight.

The very last day was the best. We went out on to the broad waters of Canoe Lake. I sat in the bow and Tom used his big bladed stick. Swish, it dipped, swoosh, it dipped, swish, swoosh, swish, swoosh. We skimmed the waters. I cannot tell why it was so, the soft wind tingling in my nostrils, brushing its way along the back of my coat, making the water laugh in little ripples, Tom joking that he couldn't light his mouth-stick, but I knew this was the best day of my life. I was with the man I loved and there was nothing special to do but be carried by the water. It was perfect.

We headed back to the shore. Tom stood up steadying himself. I was ready to spring out. Then there was a commotion in the water and Tom lost his balance.

The full weight of him fell and his head hit the gunnel* rocking the canoe. The movement turned the canoe over upside down and Tom disappeared. I never saw him again. The beautiful water hid the beautiful man.

*The gunnel is the name for the top edge of the canoe or any wooden boat.

From the shore, I watched and I watched as if by watching I would suddenly see him coming in on the light. Then I would catch him just as he used to catch the light with his paste sticks.

But in my heart I knew, our time on this earth was over. I didn't move, I didn't want anything other than to join him in the place beyond the wind. I waited and I waited until the moon showed me the way to the place where Tom's heart had gone.

Now if you ever see the dance of the northern lights, or even a shooting star, know that this light is firing from the hearts of those who loved. I was a dog who loved well.

Each of the images created by Ruth MacLean for the section on Algonquin Park is based on a painting by or, in one case a photograph, of Tom Thomson. The titles, the dates and the gallery where they can be viewed are given in the order as they appear in the book. We are very grateful to all who have helped in their contributions to this book, most especially each of the galleries where Tom's work is displayed and to Library and Archives, Canada [LAC] *, in Ottawa, which house the letters addressed to Blodwen Davies that are quoted in the Introduction to this book; to Joan Murray for her indispensable online "Tom Thomson Catalogue Raisonné" and to Elizabeth at Elizabeth's Art Gallery in Goderich for her digital work on the colour images.

Spring, Canoe Lake, spring 1916
Art Gallery of Ontario, Toronto

Photograph at Lake Scugog , 1910
Tom Thomson Art Gallery, Owen Sound

The Canoe, spring or fall 1912
Art Gallery of Ontario, Toronto

Northern Lights, summer 1915
Art Gallery of Ontario, Toronto

Campfire, fall 1916
National Gallery of Canada, Ottawa

Nocturne, fall 1915
Vancouver Art Gallery

A Rapid, spring 1915
Art Gallery of Ontario, Toronto

Wildflowers, summer 1915
McMichael Canadian Art Collection, Kleinburg

The West Wind, winter 1916-17
Art Gallery of Ontario, Toronto

Autumn, Three Trout, fall 1916
Art Gallery of Ontario, Toronto

Lightning, Canoe Lake, summer 1915
National Gallery of Canada, Ottawa

Pink Birches, summer 1915
Private Collection, Toronto

Morning, summer 1915
Tom Thomson Art Gallery, Owen Sound

Yellow Sunset, spring or summer 1916
National Gallery of Canada, Ottawa

Moonlight, fall 1915
Private Collection, Toronto

After the Storm, spring 1917
Private Collection

* http://heritage.canadiana.ca/view/oocihm.lac_reel_c4579/

48